CHARLES M. SCHULZ
creator of "Peanuts" says:

"On the wall of my studio I have an original Sunday page of B.C. given to me by Johnny Hart, and I often pause to admire it, for this page is a perfect work of comic strip art. The idea seems funnier every time I look at it, and the drawing is something for a student of comic art to study.

"Unfortunately, good drawing and fine pen technique have in these days become confused with slickness. Johnny Hart's B.C. has both good drawing, backed up with a fine pen technique, and consistently good ideas.

"I recommend it to you for fun and as a study in excellent comic strip art. I am pleased that it is now in book form, so that all of us can read and reread these many good strips."

by Johnny Hart

ABRIDGED

A FAWCETT GOLD MEDAL BOOK

Fawcett Publications, Inc., Greenwich, Conn.
Member of American Book Publishers Council, Inc.

To Irwin and Grace
who made this book possible

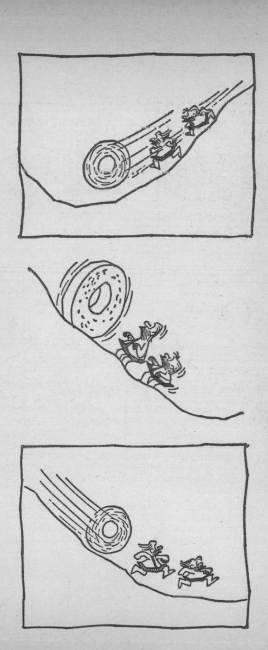

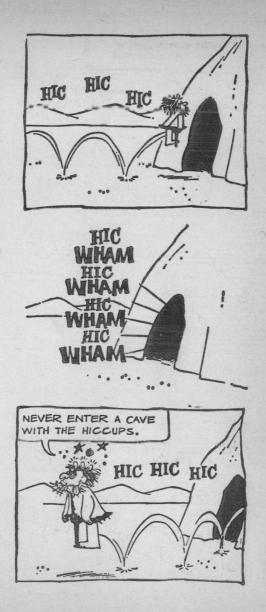

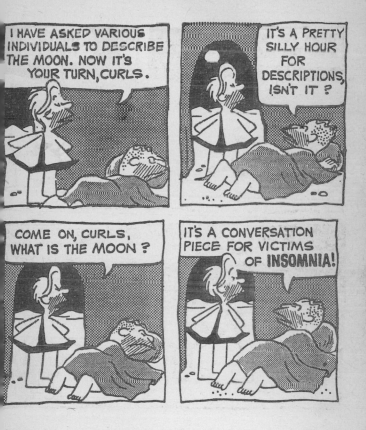

WHEN THEY GO TO ALL THAT TROUBLE, YOU DON'T HAVE THE HEART TO EAT THEM!

70-4-8